To
Anne

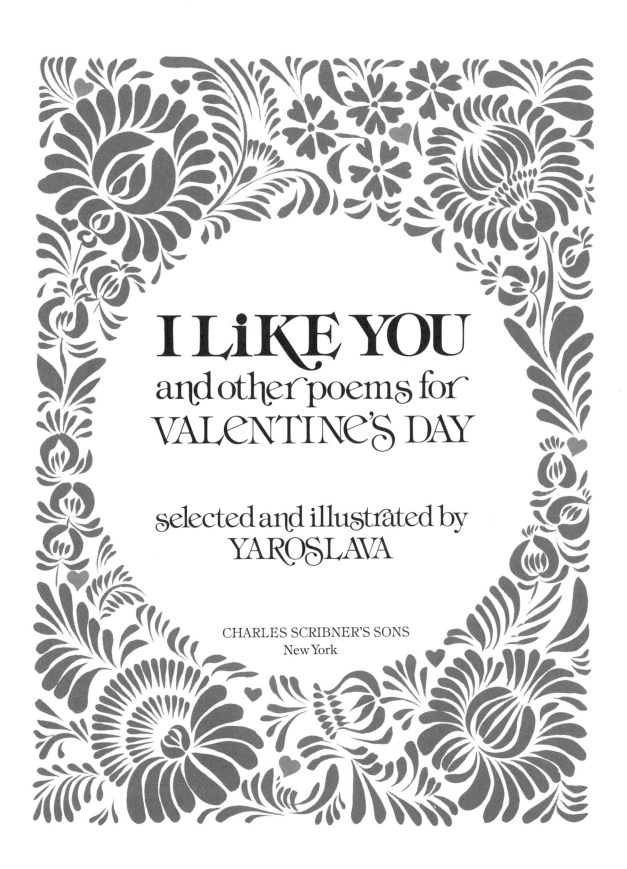

I LiKE YOU
and other poems for
VALENTINE'S DAY

selected and illustrated by
YAROSLAVA

CHARLES SCRIBNER'S SONS
New York

ACKNOWLEDGMENTS

"Bliss" by Eleanor Farjeon: From *Poems for Children* by Eleanor Farjeon.
Copyright 1938 by Eleanor Farjeon. Copyright © renewed 1966 by Gervase Farjeon.
Copyright 1951 by Eleanor Farjeon. Reprinted by permission of J. B. Lippincott Company and Harold Ober
Associates Incorporated.

"The Canal Bank" by James Stephens: From *Collected Poems* by James Stephens. Copyright 1915 by Macmillan
Publishing Co., Inc.; renewed 1943 by James Stephens. Reprinted by permission of Macmillan Publishing Co., Inc.;
also by permission of Mrs. Iris Wise, Macmillan London and Basingstoke, and The Macmillan Company of Canada
Limited.

"Hug O' War" and **"Love"** by Shel Silverstein: From *Where the Sidewalk Ends* by Shel Silverstein. Copyright ©
1974 by Shel Silverstein. Reprinted by permission of Harper & Row, Publishers, Inc.

"Juke Box Love Song" by Langston Hughes: From *Montage of a Dream Deferred* by Langston Hughes. Copyright
1951 by Langston Hughes. Reprinted by permission of Harold Ober Associates Incorporated.

"Kidnap Poem" by Nikki Giovanni: From *Re Creation* by Nikki Giovanni. Copyright © 1970 by Nikki Giovanni.
Reprinted by permission of Broadside Press.

Untitled poem #27 ("Let me tell you all about me.") by Karla Kuskin: From *Any Me I Want to Be* by Karla Kuskin.
Copyright © 1972 by Karla Kuskin. Reprinted by permission of Harper & Row, Publishers, Inc.

"Little Elegy" by Elinor Wylie: From *Collected Poems of Elinor Wylie* by Elinor Wylie. Copyright 1929 by Alfred A.
Knopf, Inc. and renewed 1957 by Edwina C. Rubenstein. Reprinted by permission of Alfred A. Knopf, Inc.

"Love Lyric, II" translated by Noel Stock: From *Love Poems of Ancient Egypt* by Ezra Pound and Noel Stock.
Copyright © 1962 by Ezra Pound and Noel Stock. Reprinted by permission of New Directions Publishing Corporation.

"Love Tight" by Ted Joans: From *Afrodisia* by Ted Joans. Copyright © 1970 by Ted Joans. Reprinted with the
permission of Farrar, Straus & Giroux, Inc.

"Notes" by Paul Engle: From *A Woman Unashamed and other poems*. Copyright © 1962, 1963, 1964, 1965 by Paul
Engle. Reprinted by permission of Random House, Inc.

"A Pavane for the Nursery" by William Jay Smith: From *New and Selected Poems* by William Jay Smith. Copyright
©1954 by William Jay Smith. Used by permission of Delacorte Press/Seymour Lawrence; also by permission of
Curtis Brown Ltd.

"The Queen" by Pablo Neruda: From *The Captain's Verses* by Pablo Neruda, translated by Donald D. Walsh.
Copyright © 1972 by Pablo Neruda and Donald D. Walsh. Reprinted by permission of New Directions Publishing
Corporation.

"The River Merchant's Wife: A Letter" by Rihauku, translated by Ezra Pound: From *Collected Shorter Poems* by
Ezra Pound. Reprinted by permission of Faber and Faber Ltd.; also from *Personae* by Ezra Pound. Copyright 1926 by
Ezra Pound. Reprinted by permission of New Directions Publishing Corporation.

"The Rose Family" by Robert Frost: From *The Poetry of Robert Frost,* edited by Edward Connery Lathem.
Copyright 1928, © 1969 by Holt, Rinehart and Winston. Copyright © 1956 by Robert Frost. Reprinted by
permission of Holt, Rinehart and Winston, Publishers, the Estate of Robert Frost, and Jonathan Cape Ltd.

"Valentine" by Donald Hall: From *Exiles and Marriages* by Donald Hall. Copyright © 1955 by Donald Hall.
Reprinted by permission of Curtis Brown, Ltd.

"Variations on a Cosmical Air" by Malcolm Cowley: From *Blue Juanita: Collected Poems* by Malcolm Cowley.
Copyright © 1968 by Malcolm Cowley. Reprinted by permission of Viking Penguin, Inc.

"A Variation on 'To Say to Go to Sleep'" adapted from a poem by Rainer Maria Rilke by Randall Jarrell: From
The Complete Poems by Randall Jarrell. Copyright © 1935, 1936, 1937, 1940, 1941, 1942, 1944, 1945, 1946, 1947, 1948,
1949, 1950, 1951, 1952, 1965, 1966, 1967, 1968, 1969 by Mrs. Randall Jarrell. Copyright renewed 1968, 1969 by Mrs.
Randall Jarrell. Reprinted with the permission of W. W. Norton & Company, Inc.

"We Could Be Friends" by Myra Cohn Livingston: From *The Way Things Are and other poems* (A Margaret K.
McElderry Book). Reprinted by permission of Atheneum Publishers and McIntosh and Otis, Inc.

Library of Congress Cataloging in Publication Data
Main entry under title: I like you and other poems for Valentine's Day.
SUMMARY: A collection of poems of love and affection by a variety of poets.
1. Love poetry. [1. Love poetry. 2. Poetry—Collections] I. Yaroslava, pseud.
PN6110.L6I2   808.81'9'354   76-45807   ISBN 0-684-14746-7

CONTENTS

from VARIATIONS ON A COSMICAL AIR

. . . . .

Love is the flower of a day,
love is a rosebud—anyway,
when we propound its every feature,
we make it sound like horticulture,
and even in our puberty
we drown love in philosophy.

"But I'm coming around in a taxi honey,
　Tomorrow night with a roll of money
　You wanna be ready 'bout ha-past eight."

Malcolm Cowley

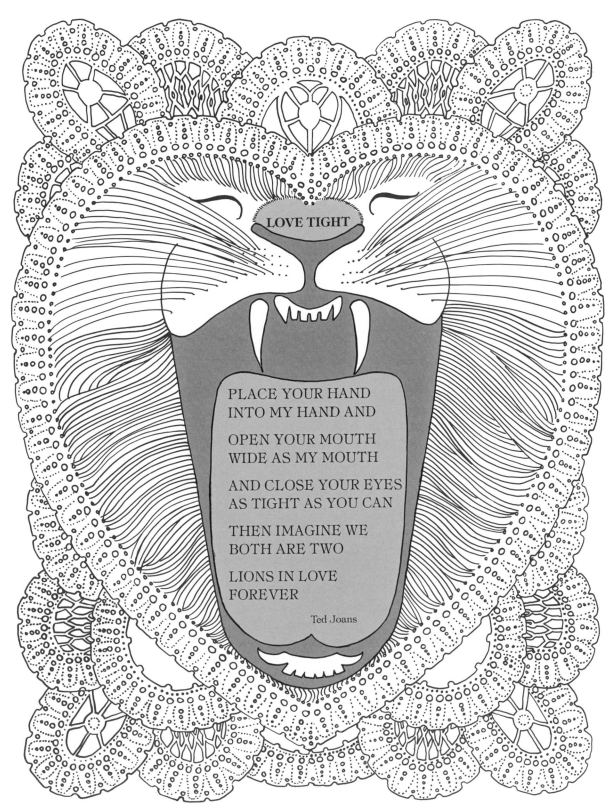

LOVE TIGHT

PLACE YOUR HAND
INTO MY HAND AND

OPEN YOUR MOUTH
WIDE AS MY MOUTH

AND CLOSE YOUR EYES
AS TIGHT AS YOU CAN

THEN IMAGINE WE
BOTH ARE TWO

LIONS IN LOVE
FOREVER

Ted Joans

MY VALENTINE

I will make you brooches
And toys for your delight
Of bird song at morning
And starshine at night.
I will build a palace
Fit for you and me,

Of green days in forests
And blue days at sea.

Robert Louis Stevenson

6

NOTES

Butterfly trembles when the wind blows.
You walk near me.
The dog barks at the loud moon.
When you come to me,
I speak softly, softly,
Until we are silent together.
For two hundred years
This pine tree has been trained to grow sideways.
I have known you only one week,
But I bend as you walk toward me.

Paul Engle

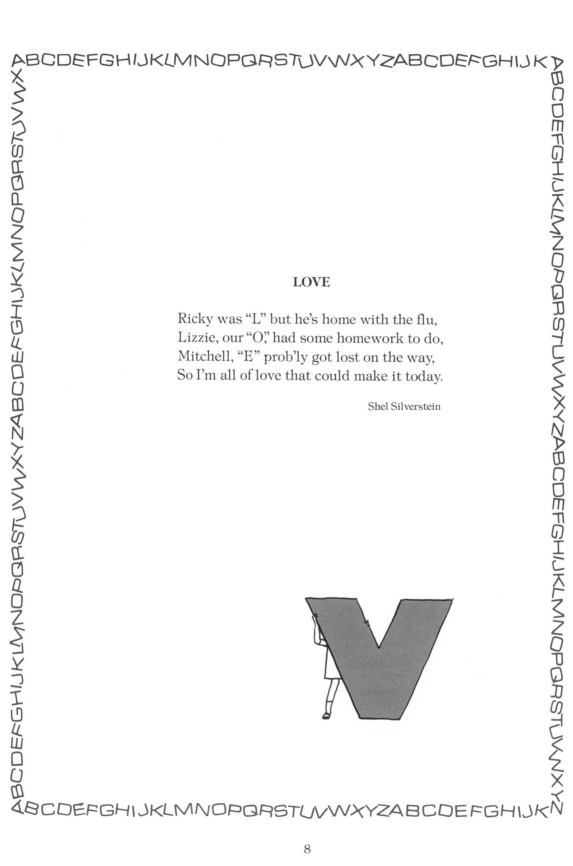

LOVE

Ricky was "L" but he's home with the flu,
Lizzie, our "O," had some homework to do,
Mitchell, "E" prob'ly got lost on the way,
So I'm all of love that could make it today.

Shel Silverstein

I'll love you till Heaven
Rips the stars from his coat,
And the Moon rows away in
A glass-bottomed boat;
And Orion steps down
Like a diver below,
And Earth is ablaze,
And Ocean aglow.

So touch the air softly,
And swing the broom high.
We will dust the gray mountains,
And sweep the blue sky;
And I'll love you as long
As the furrow the plow,
As However is Ever,
And Ever is Now.

William Jay Smith

11

VALENTINE

Chipmunks jump, and
Greensnakes slither.
Rather burst than
Not be with her.

Bluebirds fight, but
Bears are stronger.
We've got fifty
Years or longer.

Hoptoads hop, but
Hogs are fatter.
Nothing else but
Us can matter.

Donald Hall

THE CANAL BANK

I know a girl,
And a girl knows me,
And the owl says, what!
And the owl says, who?

But what we know
We both agree
That nobody else
Shall hear or see;

It's all between herself and me:
To wit? said the owl,
To woo! said I,
To-what! To-wit! To-woo!

James Stephens

13

Old woman, old woman, shall we go a shearing?
Speak a little louder, Sir, I'm very thick of hearing.

Old woman, old woman, shall we go a gleaning?
Speak a little louder, Sir, I cannot tell your meaning.

Old woman, old woman, shall we go a walking?
Speak a little louder, Sir, or what's the use of talking?

Old woman, old woman, shall I kiss you dearly?
Thank you, kind Sir, I hear you very clearly.

Mother Goose

LAVENDER'S BLUE

Lavender's blue, dilly, dilly, lavender's green,
    When I'm a King, dilly, dilly, you shall be Queen;
Who told you so, dilly, dilly, who told you so?
    'Twas mine own heart, dilly, dilly, that told me so.

Call up your men, dilly, dilly, set them to work,
    Some with a rake, dilly, dilly, some with a fork;
Some to make hay, dilly, dilly, some to thresh corn,
    While you and I, dilly, dilly, keep ourselves warm.

If it should hap, dilly, dilly, if it should chance,
    We shall be gay, dilly, dilly, we shall both dance;
Lavender's blue, dilly, dilly, lavender's green,
    When I'm a King, dilly, dilly, you shall be Queen.

Anonymous

LOVE LYRIC, II

Nothing, nothing can keep me from my love
Standing on the other shore.

Not even old crocodile
There on the sandbank between us
Can keep us apart.

I go in spite of him,
I walk upon the waves,
Her love flows back across the water,
Turning waves to solid earth
For me to walk on.

The river is our Enchanted Sea.

translated from the ancient Egyptian
by Noel Stock

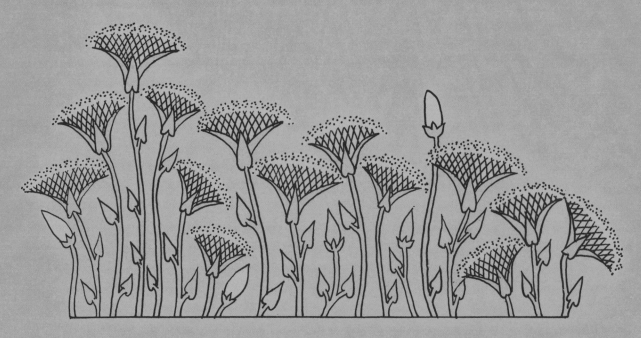

16

KIDNAP POEM

ever been kidnapped
by a poet
if i were a poet
i'd kidnap you
put you in my phrases and meter
you to jones beach
or maybe coney island
or maybe just to my house
lyric you in lilacs
dash you in the rain
blend into the beach
to complement my see
play the lyre for you
ode you with my love song
anything to win you
wrap you in the red Black green
show you off to mama
yeah if i were a poet i'd kid
nap you

Nikki Giovanni

WE COULD BE FRIENDS

We could be friends
Like friends are supposed to be.
You, picking up the telephone
Calling me
    to come over and play
    or take a walk,
    finding a place
    to sit and talk,
Or just goof around
Like friends do,
Me, picking up the telephone
Calling you.

Myra Cohn Livingston

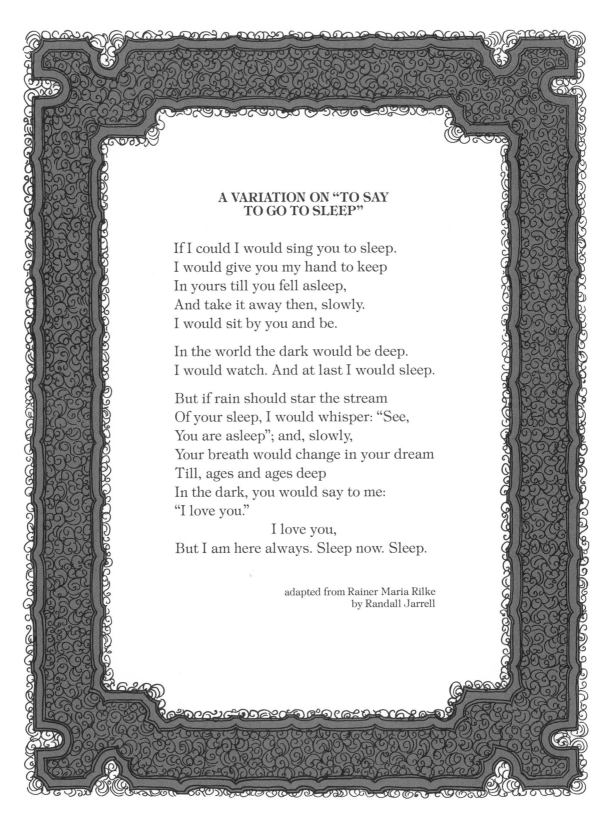

**A VARIATION ON "TO SAY
TO GO TO SLEEP"**

If I could I would sing you to sleep.
I would give you my hand to keep
In yours till you fell asleep,
And take it away then, slowly.
I would sit by you and be.

In the world the dark would be deep.
I would watch. And at last I would sleep.

But if rain should star the stream
Of your sleep, I would whisper: "See,
You are asleep"; and, slowly,
Your breath would change in your dream
Till, ages and ages deep
In the dark, you would say to me:
"I love you."
                    I love you,
But I am here always. Sleep now. Sleep.

adapted from Rainer Maria Rilke
by Randall Jarrell

20

THE QUEEN

I have named you queen.
There are taller ones than you, taller.
There are purer ones than you, purer.
There are lovelier than you, lovelier.

But you are the queen.

When you go through the streets
no one recognizes you.
No one sees your crystal crown, no one looks
at the carpet of red gold
that you tread as you pass,
the nonexistent carpet.

And when you appear
all the rivers sound
in my body, bells
shake the sky,
and a hymn fills the world.

Only you and I,
only you and I, my love,
listen to it.

Pablo Neruda
translated by Donald D. Walsh

THE ROSE FAMILY

The rose is a rose,
And was always a rose,
But the theory now goes
That the apple's a rose,
And the pear is, and so's
The plum, I suppose.
The dear only knows
What will next prove a rose.
You, of course, are a rose—
But were always a rose.

Robert Frost

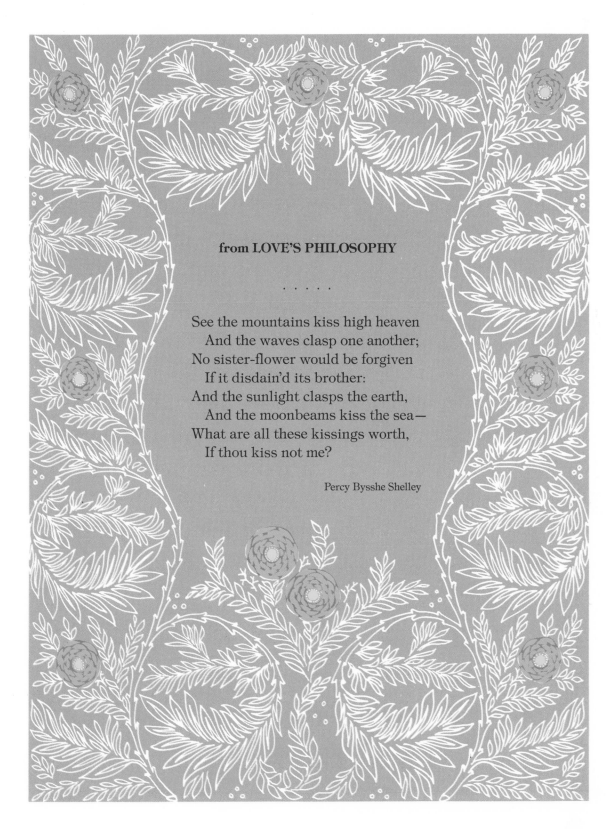

from LOVE'S PHILOSOPHY

. . . . .

See the mountains kiss high heaven
  And the waves clasp one another;
No sister-flower would be forgiven
  If it disdain'd its brother:
And the sunlight clasps the earth,
  And the moonbeams kiss the sea—
What are all these kissings worth,
  If thou kiss not me?

Percy Bysshe Shelley

THE RIVER-MERCHANT'S WIFE:
A LETTER

While my hair was still cut straight across my forehead
I played about the front gate, pulling flowers.
You came by on bamboo stilts, playing horse,
You walked about my seat, playing with blue plums.
And we went on living in the village of Chokan:
Two small people, without dislike or suspicion.

At fourteen I married My Lord you.
I never laughed, being bashful.
Lowering my head, I looked at the wall.
Called to, a thousand times, I never looked back.

At fifteen I stopped scowling,
I desired my dust to be mingled with yours
For ever and for ever and for ever,
Why should I climb the look out?

At sixteen you departed,
You went into far Ku-to-yen, by the river of swirling eddies,
And you have been gone five months.
The monkeys make sorrowful noise overhead.

You dragged your feet when you went out.
By the gate now, the moss is grown, the different mosses,
Too deep to clear them away!
The leaves fall early this autumn, in wind.
The paired butterflies are already yellow with August
Over the grass in the West garden;
They hurt me. I grow older.
If you are coming down through the narrows of the
    river Kiang,
Please let me know beforehand,
And I will come out to meet you
    As far as Cho-fu-Sa.

Rihauku
translated by Ezra Pound

24

HUG O' WAR

I will not play at tug o' war.
I'd rather play at hug o' war,
Where everyone hugs
Instead of tugs,
Where everyone giggles
And rolls on the rug,
Where everyone kisses,
And everyone grins,
And everyone cuddles,
And everyone wins.

Shel Silverstein

JUKE BOX LOVE SONG

I could take the Harlem night
and wrap around you,
Take the neon lights and make a crown,
Take the Lenox Avenue buses,
Taxis, subways,
And for your love song tone their rumble down.
Take Harlem's heartbeat,
Make a drumbeat,
Put it on a record, let it whirl,
And while we listen to it play,
Dance with you till day—
Dance with you, my sweet brown Harlem girl.

Langston Hughes

Let me tell you all about me.
Children love me,
You're a child.
All my heads are green and handsome.
All my eyes are red and wild.
All my toes have claws upon them.
All the claws have hooks.
I blow smoke through all my noses.
It is hotter than it looks.
All my tails have points upon them.
All my teeth are sharp and blue.
I won't bite you very badly.
I am fond of you.
All my scales are shaped like arrows.
They will hurt you if you touch.
So, although I know you'll love me,
Do not pet me very much.

Karla Kuskin

BLISS

Let me fetch sticks,
Let me fetch stones,
Throw me your bones,
Teach me your tricks.

When you go ride,
Let me go run,
You in the sun,
Me at your side;

When you go swim,
Let me go too
Both lost in blue
Up to the brim;

Let me do this,
Let me do that—
What you are at,
That is my bliss.

Eleanor Farjeon

TAKE A LUMP OF CLAY

Take a lump of clay,
Wet it, pat it,
Make a statue of you
And a statue of me.
Then shatter them, clatter them,
Add some water,
And break them and mold them
Into a statue of you
And a statue of me.
Then, in mine, there are bits of you
And in you there are bits of me.
Nothing shall ever keep us apart.

Kuan Tao Sheng (Sung Dynasty)

I LIKE YOU

Although I saw you
The day before yesterday,
And yesterday and today,
This much is true—
I want to see you tomorrow, too!

Masuhito (8th Century)